Crow flew high and then higher.
Soon, Crow was too hot.

He flew lower among the shady trees.
"This is better," Crow thought.

Crow still had a long way to fly
home to see his mother.
He flew over fields and hills.

"I am very thirsty," Crow thought, but he kept flying. Finally, Crow was so thirsty that his wings were weak.

Crow landed on the ground.
"I cannot hop all the way home,"
Crow thought.

"It is too far, and this is dangerous for me.
I *must* find water!"

Crow found a jug. In the bottom,
there was water!

Crow poked his beak into the jug.
He could not reach the water.

Crow flapped a wing inside the jug.
He could not reach the water.

Poor Crow! He was so thirsty, and he wanted to fly home. Crow pushed a stick into the jug but it did not reach the water.

Crow was desperate. He was going to hop away. Then he remembered what his mother told him. "Never stop trying," he said.

I will not quit, thought Crow.
He picked up a pebble and dropped it
into the jug.

Then he tossed in another pebble.
Still he could not reach the water.

Crow was so thirsty that his throat hurt.
"I will not quit," thought Crow.

He tossed many more pebbles in.
Slowly the water rose.

Finally, Crow could touch the water.
He drank all of it!
He was very glad he had kept trying.